Class No. J636.7   Acc No. C/226545
Author: goldsack, G   Loc: 1 1 JUL 2013

LEABHARLANN
CHONDAE AN CHABHAIN

1. This book may be kept three weeks. It is to be
   returned on / befo ~~red below.~~
2. A fine of 50c will b   J636.7 / C226545   art
   of week a book is   30018002240428   e 23)

2 2 NOV 2013		
1 7 NOV 2014		
2 9 DEC 2014		

Favourite Pets

by Gabby Goldsack

ticktock MEDIA

Copyright © **ticktock** Entertainment Ltd 2004

First published in Great Britain in 2004 by **ticktock** Media Ltd.,
Unit 2, Orchard Business Centre, North Farm Road, Tunbridge Wells, Kent, TN2 3XF

We would like to thank: Meme Ltd.

Every effort has been made to trace the copyright holders, and we apologise in advance for any unintentional omissions.
We would be pleased to insert the appropriate acknowledgements in any subsequent edition of this publication.

ISBN 1 86007 446 4 HB
ISBN 1 86007 442 1 PB

Printed in China

Contents

Learning Advice

This book is designed to be both stimulating and accessible to young readers. Young children can show a wide range in ability. This is not necessarily a guide to later levels of achievement. Young children learn well through sharing. Therefore, each activity in this book should be treated as an opportunity to share and talk about what is on each page. At this age, all reading should be shared reading. By showing a child that you find reading exciting, you will pass this positive image on to your child. Try to involve your child in each story as much as possible, ask and answer questions, and talk about any ideas that arise. Encourage your child to come up with ideas on his or her own. Many books on pets are available at your local library.

Favourite Pets:
Indoor Pets

Pets are animals that people keep at their homes.
Many animals make good pets. Some pets are kept indoors.
Some live in cages or tanks and others walk around freely.

Dogs are fun pets. People can train their dogs to obey commands and sometimes to do tricks. A baby dog is called a **puppy**.

nose

A pet **hamster** is active and needs an exercise wheel in its **cage**. Hamsters sleep in the day and wake up at night.

Cats are common pets. Their fur is either long and silky or short and soft. A baby cat is called a **kitten**.

beak

A pet **budgie** lives in a **cage** indoors. Sometimes budgies can be taught to say words!

eye

Goldfish are easy to look after. They can live for a long time if they are properly fed and their **tanks** are kept clean.

Pet Words

Can you find these words on the page?

puppy

kitten

cage

eye

nose

tanks

Favourite Pets:
Outdoor Pets

Some pets need to live outdoors. Animals that live outdoors are often bigger than those that live indoors and need a lot more space.

The **tortoise** is very **slow** at eating, walking and moving around. Pet tortoises can live as long as 60 or even 90 years! Some tortoises have to sleep all winter.

A pet **rabbit** lives in a hutch but sometimes needs to run free in the garden. A wild rabbit lives in a **burrow**.

ears

Many people think that **pigs** are dirty animals but they are actually very clean. A healthy pig eats a lot.

Some people keep horses so they can **ride** them. The smallest **horse** is called a *falabella*. Falabellas are less than 80 cm tall. A baby horse is called a **foal**.

horns

A **goat** is a very useful pet because it keeps grass short by eating it. Goats also produce **milk** that people can drink and make into cheese!

Pet Words

Can you find these words on the page?

ride

foal

ears

horns

slow

milk

Word Puzzles

Look at these animal pictures.
Can you put the words in the right order?

goes

The

"woof"

1

Pet Words

You have seen these words before. Use the pictures to help you say them.

ears

nose

cat

"meow"

2

The

"cheep"

The

budgie

3

eye

beak

horns

A Story to Read:
The Best Dog

Rover the dog was hungry. He wanted to be fed but his owner, Oliver, was reading a new book. It was all about **dogs**.

Oliver's book had many different types of dogs in it. Some of the dogs had spots. There were even some dogs that were many different colours. Some of the dogs had special jobs.

10

All of the dogs were different. They looked like they would be fun to play with. Rover was worried. He thought Oliver wanted a new dog.

Later, Oliver's mum was on the telephone. She was talking to the **pet-shop owner**. Rover sadly chewed on his bone.

Oliver was getting
a new dog.
Rover knew it
must be true.
It could be a
big, mean dog.
What would
Rover do?

Oliver's mum
came home
with a box
under her arm.
The new dog
must be very
small, Rover
thought.

Rover couldn't look. He wanted to hide. Then, Oliver lifted something out of the box. It was a brand new dog bed for Rover! It looked so comfortable!

Oliver put the bed in Rover's favourite sleeping spot. "You are the best dog in the world," Oliver said, and he gave Rover a big hug.

Can you answer these questions about the story you have just read?

1 What was Oliver's new book about?
2 Who was Oliver's mum talking to on the phone?
3 What was in the box?

A Story to Share:
The Great Food Hunt

Can you say the words in **bold**? Use the pictures to help you.

Carla the cat eats fish for breakfast, lunch and **dinner**.

"Meooow," says Carla. "I eat fish all the time! I wonder if other animals eat food that is tastier than fish?"

14

"Woof, woof," says Daisy the dog. "Try one of my big, yummy **bones**!" Carla tries to nibble a bone, but it is too hard for her to bite.

"Cheep, cheep," says Beryl the budgie. "My birdseed is the best." Carla eats a few seeds, but they do not taste good to her.

"Snuffle, snuffle," says Roland the rabbit. "Try this crunchy **carrot**." Carla tries to bite the carrot, but her teeth are too little.

"Sunflower seeds are perfect for storing in your cheeks," says Hank the hamster. But Carla doesn't want to store food in her cheeks. She just wants to eat it!

"Crisp, green **lettuce** is my favourite food." says Tammy the tortoise.

"I don't really like lettuce," says Carla.

So, Carla goes back to her dish. "I think the best food for cats is **fish** after all!"

17

Pet Game:
What's for Lunch?

All pets need to be fed! Can you help the hungry tortoise reach the lettuce?

This exciting game is for 2 to 4 players!

First, find a small plastic toy for each player. Place each toy on the start line. Then, roll a dice to see who goes first. The player who rolls the highest number goes first.

Take turns moving along the spaces, counting as you go. Follow the instructions on the spaces that you land on. The first person to reach the lettuce wins!

START

1

9
Clean your rabbit's hutch. Hop forward 2 spaces.

8

10

11

FINISH
Hooray! You're the first to reach the lettuce. You win!

18

18

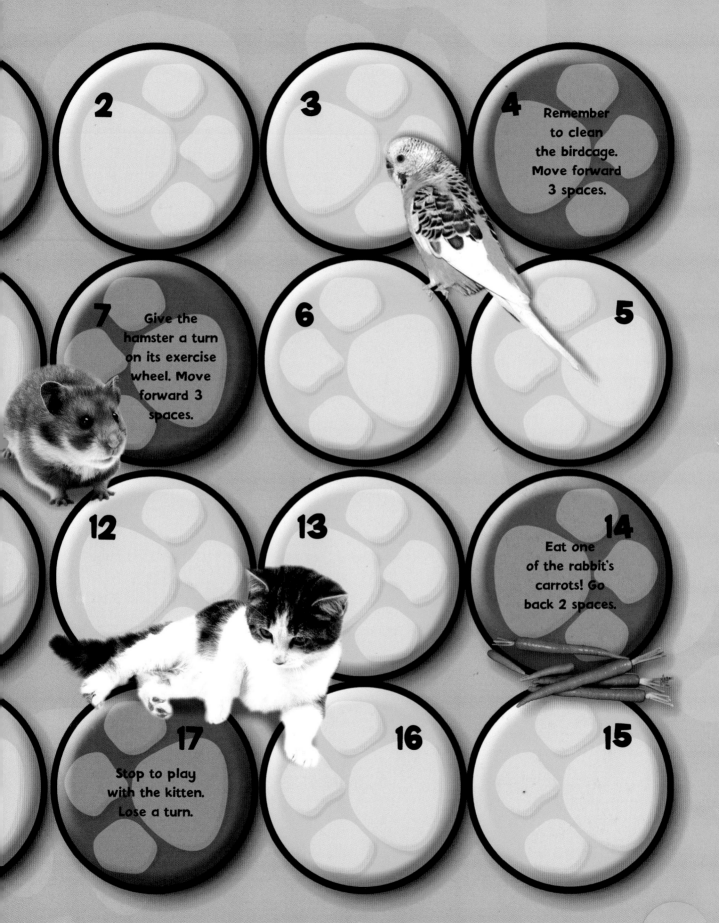

2

3

4 Remember to clean the birdcage. Move forward 3 spaces.

7 Give the hamster a turn on its exercise wheel. Move forward 3 spaces.

6

5

12

13

14 Eat one of the rabbit's carrots! Go back 2 spaces.

17 Stop to play with the kitten. Lose a turn.

16

15

19

A Bedtime Story:
A Pet for Harry

One day, Harry watched his big sister, Amy, cuddle her new kitten. Amy named the kitten *Tiger*. Harry thought that Tiger looked like fun.

"Can I have a pet of my own?" Harry asked his mum.

"Of course," said Mum. "But you must look after it."

"And give it lots of cuddles," added Amy.

That afternoon, Mum took Harry and Amy to the pet shop. The shopkeeper showed them lots of different pets.

"What kind of pet would you like?" asked Mum.

"How about a kitten?" said Amy. Harry thought for a while and then shook his head.

"A kitten would be nice," he said, "but it may fight Tiger."

They walked around the shop, then stopped in front of a dog. It had a fluffy coat and big, brown eyes.

"Ah, he looks cute," said Amy.

"Yes! How about a puppy?" said Mum.

"Well, he does look cuddly," agreed Harry, "but he will get big and need to be walked lots."

"And he may chase Tiger," added Amy.

Next, they saw a budgie. It had beautiful green feathers and made lots of noise.

"Well, a budgie won't grow big," said Mum, "and you won't need to take it for walks." Harry stroked the budgie's feathers, then shook his head.

"He's not very cuddly," he said. "And he's too noisy."

"And Tiger might try to catch him," added Amy.

The shopkeeper showed them a hamster. He was peeping out of his little house.

"He looks cuddly," said Amy.

The shopkeeper took the hamster out of its cage and handed it to Harry. Harry held the hamster gently.

"He is quite cuddly," he said.

"Hamsters sleep a lot during the day," said the shopkeeper.

"And wake up at night," added Mum.

"Then a hamster is not for me," decided Harry.

There were lots of fish swimming around in a big tank. Some of them were gold, some were black and gold, and some were silver and gold.

"They are pretty," said Mum.

"How about a goldfish?" she asked Harry.

"They're very easy to look after," explained the shopkeeper.

"But they're not at all cuddly," said Harry, "and you can't play with them."

"And Tiger might try to catch them," added Amy.

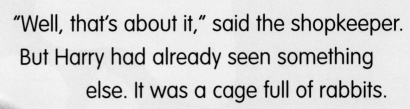

"Well, that's about it," said the shopkeeper. But Harry had already seen something else. It was a cage full of rabbits. There were black rabbits and white rabbits. There were rabbits with long, pointy ears, and there were rabbits with long, floppy ears.

"Rabbits are cuddly and fun," said Harry. "A rabbit would be the perfect pet for me." It didn't take Harry long to choose a rabbit. He was white and cuddly and very, very friendly. Harry decided to name the rabbit *Snowy*.

Harry took the rabbit home, and carried it into the garden. He gave Snowy some food and water.

"You're my new best friend," Harry whispered. "I think we're going to have lots and lots of fun."

Pet Counting:
Pet Line-up

How many pets are there in each line? Can you count them?

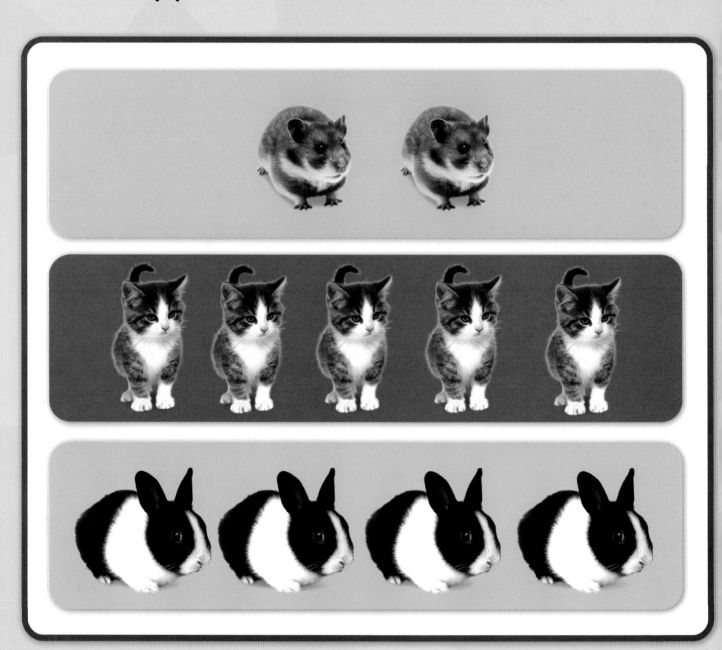

Which line has the most pets in it? Which line has the least?

Number words

One
Two
Three
Four
Five
Six

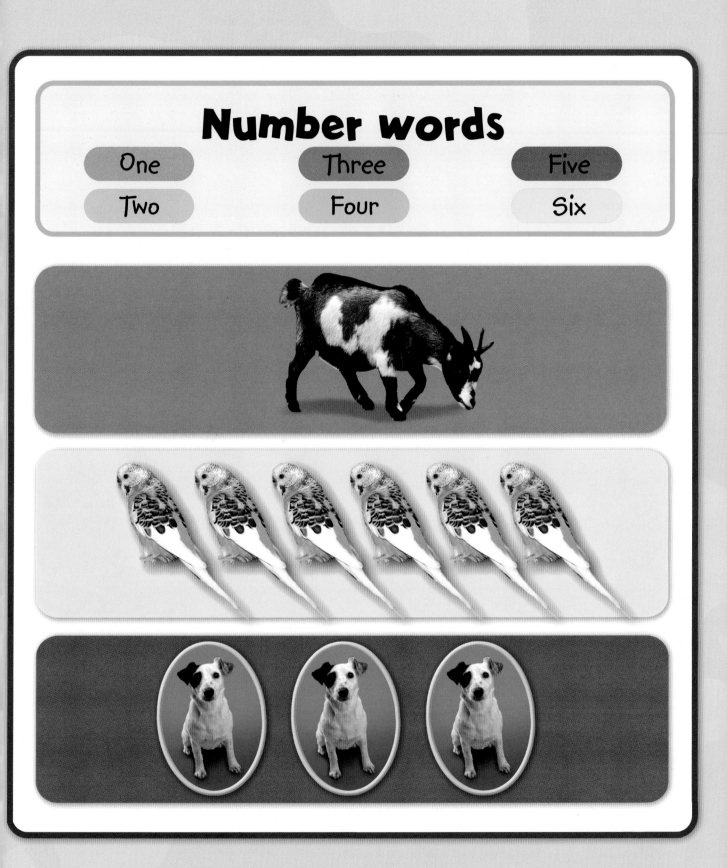

Can you match the number words to the right number of animals?

Pet Counting:
Pet Care

Mother cats and dogs often have lots of babies to care for. Which mother pet has the most babies?

How many puppies does the dog have?

How many kittens does the cat have?

It's dinner time for the animals! Can you match the pets up with their favourite food? Count the food bowls for a clue.

Which animal has the most for dinner?

Which animal has the least?

Spot
the Difference

A veterinarian is an animal doctor. Vets are good at finding out what is wrong with your pet.

Look at these two pictures.
Can you spot the four differences between them?

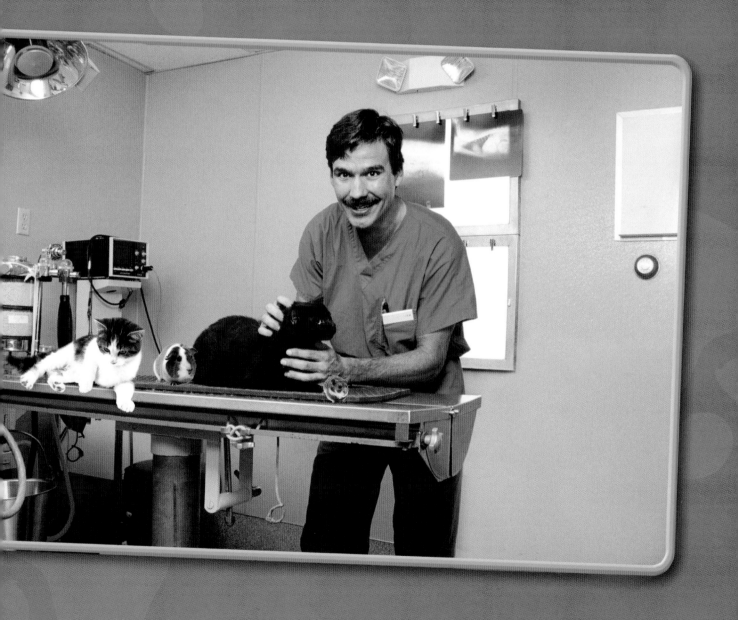

Spot the Difference answers: 1. The vet's stethoscope is missing. **2.** The vet's shirt is a different colour. **3.** The budgie on the vet's arm is missing. **4.** The dog is gone.

29

Make a
Pet Mask

Pet cats and dogs are cute. Make a pet mask and pretend you are your favourite pet!

> **You will need:** **1.** scissors (and an adult to use them) **2.** string or elastic **3.** colouring pens or pencils **4.** a piece of card big enough to cover your face

cat   dog   mouse

1. Choose which pet you want to be.

2. Using the pictures above to help you, copy your chosen pet face on to the mask.

3. Colour in your pet mask any way you want to.

4. Ask an adult to cut around the mask shape and cut out the eye holes.

5. Then ask the adult to push holes through the side of the mask with scissors as shown.

6. Thread the piece of string through the holes and tie a knot as shown. Ask an adult to help you adjust the string to fit your head.

Try looking at your pets and how they behave.

Now you can copy them. What sounds do they make? How do they move?

Word Finder

Here are some of the words used in this book. Can you remember what they mean? Go back and look through the book to see if you can find each word again.

bones   pig   food

hamster   goldfish   eye

cheese   budgie   horns

beak   tanks   puppy

rabbit   slow   milk

cat   cage   kitten

dog   carrot   lettuce